MEANWHILE

BACK AT THE VESTRY . . .

MEANWHILE,

BACK AT THE VESTRY . . .

By

REG FRARY

with illustrations by

Madeleine R. Forster

NORHEIMSUND BOOKS AND CARDS
1 Whitney Road
Burton Latimer
Kettering
Northamptonshire NN15 5SL

By the same author
DON'T UPSET THE CHOIR
WHAT ABOUT THE CHOIR, VICAR ?
HAVE YOU HEARD OUR CHOIR ?
DON'T BLAME THE ORGANIST
CHOIRS INFERNAL
REALLY, VICAR !
(formerly entitled "Laughter in Church")

ISBN 0 948852 52 6

PREFACE

IF I had not spent all these years as an English Church chorister, how else would I have liked to spend the time ? I have no doubts at all. I'd have loved to have been good enough to be a player in an Austrian brass band – surely among the finest in the world. For me there is something wondrous, thrilling, about the sound of those bands that, whenever I hear it, wherever I am, excites and exalts my spirit and brings me back over the miles and over the years to the magic of the mountains and lakes of lovely Austria – to the gloomy majesty of the Wilder Kaiser peaks, to the crystal brightness of the sudden reds and golds in a summer sunset over Lake Zell as it points with fiery fingers to towering storm clouds approaching beyond the mountains.

Would I have written about life behind the scenes with an Austrian brass band as I do about English church choirs ? It would have been a joy for me. The two sources of music have much in common – the traditional outward formality of appearance, the wonderful inside camaraderie.

Even in the most sweltering summer weather, when their audience droops and sprawls around them with sandals or bare feet and sloppy shorts and singlets and sunglasses, the band plays on with supreme disregard for the heat, the men immaculately attired, colourful, correct, the band girls, so talented, so attractive, splendidly uniformed and plumed. Ah ! formality – how grand it can be !

And after the concert is over, in the band room away from the crowds, what goes on then ? Something, I am sure, very much akin to what goes on in the choir vestry when the service is finished. That's when the formal facade would be lifted. That's where the humour and drama of a close, dedicated company would be. That's what I'd write about.

But I dream. I'm not an Austrian bandsman, I'm an English choirman and there are more choir vestries to be investigated . . .

HORSE SENSE

IT is a popular practice in the diocese in which my friend Alf is organist and choirmaster at a most unfashionable, end-of-the-line red brick church, for various church choirs to be invited to sing Evensong at the cathedral while the regular choir are on summer vacation.

Alf's choir are never invited. This is generally thought to be because no-one at the cathedral has ever heard of them, although the new sidesman who is very embittered about the music at the church reckons it's because someone at the cathedral *has* heard of them. The new sidesman is very embittered because he recently moved into the area and found it most difficult to locate a suitable church to which he might attach himself. Of the three in the neighbourhood, one was closed and being converted into luxury town flats (all with cable T.V. and imitation log fires), one had Sunday services that reminded him of scout jamborees and the third had Alf's choir. Eventually he had decided that Alf's choir was slightly the lesser of two evils and the vicar was very nice and offered him a job as sidesman. So he joined the church to see what would happen. He hoped he could brave it out with the choir but realised how much he was asking of himself. At his former church the choir had sung beautiful unaccompanied Mediaeval and Tudor music that had soothed and uplifted his spirit whereas Alf's choir were always singing dreadful Victorian anthems at full blast that made his teeth ache.

During a recent visit to Alf I took my place in the choir at Sunday Matins as usual and was delighted that for the anthem we were bellowing something by one of my favourite Victorian composers, Sir George Elvey, a long, rattling good piece, all sugary quartets and solos and heroic choruses. Elvey was organist at St.

George's Chapel, Windsor Castle and Organist to Her Majesty during a considerable period in the nineteenth century and although 'those who know' may believe that his only lasting contribution to English church music is his tune '*St. George*' to the harvest hymn 'Come ye thankful people come' I have always derived the greatest pleasure from singing in any performance of his works that have come my way. I have a very soft spot for Sir George.

At the end of the anthem the choir knelt down exhilarated and well satisfied with their efforts while the vicar led the prayers 'for all sorts and conditions of men, and especially on this St. Cecilia's day, for all musicians - those singers and instrumentalists who give us so much pleasure through their talents'. He coughed and dropped his book. 'Also our choir and organist' he added.

In the choir vestry after the service when everyone was hastily hanging up their robes on a row of broken pegs and bent nails or flinging them over the backs of equally broken and bent chairs Alf called us together round the battered piano and said he had some unexpected news for us. We had been invited - indeed begged - by the vicar of a church some miles away to sing at a special service next Sunday afternoon. 'The trouble seems to be that someone there has got their dates mixed up' explained Alf. 'Their choir is booked to sing three o'clock Evensong at the cathedral and at the same time there's this Horseman's Sunday service at the church. They're expecting scores of people and horses - and they'll expect a choir as well'.

For a moment the response was silence except for one of our basses who said "Rubbish" but he had been in the choir for 50 years and always said "Rubbish" when anyone mentioned doing anything out of the ordinary. And this situation was admittedly something very much out of the ordinary, particularly in view of the fact that the choir of the church seeking our help was one of those that sang the kind of music beloved of our new sidesman and were always winning

8

prizes at important music festivals and giving recitals at inflated entrance prices in aid of the organ fund, whereas our choir never went near a music festival and no-one had ever paid anything to hear us sing. "Well, what about it?" asked Alf. "Shall we have a go?"

"Does the Vicar know about this?" asked someone.

"Course" assured Alf "He was the one who got the phone call from *their* vicar. "The vicar told me just before the service this morning".

"What did he say?" asked the same questioner.

"Oh, the usual" confirmed Alf. "He thought the idea great, wonderful - and something to do with inter-church fellowship".

"When he saw me just before the service" supplied a flamboyantly decorative soprano who was arranging cascading blond hair before the cracked vestry mirror "he said, How lovely. He always says How lovely, when he sees me".

"Heaven help us" retorted a large contralto lady dressed entirely in dark brown with dark brown corrugated hair.

The rubbishing bass spoke again. "Rubbish", he said, "and besides our choir wouldn't fit in with a congregation used to hearing all that Mediaeval wailing stuff. They wouldn't understand our good, hearty singing".

"But we wouldn't have their usual congregation" pointed out the decorative choirgirl excitedly. "We'd have all those horsey people and I've got an idea that horsey people don't go in much for Mediaeval music - at least, the drayman down at the brewery stables don't. My uncle works there and what they sing in the bar on Saturday nights isn't Medieval at all."

"Well, there you are!" beamed Alf. "We wouldn't actually do drinking songs but we could do some Elvey. I reckon they'd like that..."

The horsey service was the most enjoyable the choir could remember for years. It was a kind of choral Evensong with the usual canticles replaced with hymns - well known, roaring rollicking hymns all about heavenly armies coming down hard and heavy on evil hordes.

As the church emptied after the service the scene outside resembled a late Victorian painting, with horse carriages, brewers' drays, horse busses, costers' carts and people on horse-back dispersing in a clattering colourful jumble. And quite a crowd of well-wishers gathered at the choir vestry door as we came out, They were all saying nice extravagant things about our singing, and our solo tenor, an ardent opera-goer was so moved that he declared it was all like being outside the stage door of the Royal Opera House after a gala performance. A gaunt unendingly tall immaculately attired lady of uncertain age leading a heavyweight hunter barged through the crowd and grasped the first hand she came across - which happened to be mine. Applying a paralising grip she announced "Splendid show - stirring stuff - right sort of hymns. And the 'er anthem thing - I've never heard anything like it in my life. What was it?" And Alf, always ready to help in the public relations department, butted in to say that our choir specialised in singing the type of music, and giving the type of performance, rarely heard in church today, so if she joined our church she could enjoy it every Sunday.

Back in our church a week or two after our 'great touring triumph' as Alf insisted on calling our emergency visit, the unexpected was still with us. As we assembled for choral Matins our operatically inclined tenor came into the vestry excitedly and announced "There are a lot of those horsey people in church". "Rubbish" said the bass.

"There are two pews of them" insisted the tenor "and a horse tied to the railings around the back".

"They've come to hear us again - they know a good thing when they come across it" beamed the decorative soprano edging the corrugated contralto from the cracked mirror.

The vicar, never missing a new face in church, had immediately welcomed the newcomers in his usual lovely, enthusiastic, swamping chummy manner that had successfully shattered the confidence of many a potential new member of the

10

congregation who had summoned up the courage to attend a service at an unfamiliar church - "Great - splendid - well, well come on, do come up closer to the others. And there's coffee afterwards and you must meet us all - a really jolly bunch. Ah! we don't take no for an answer here. See you after the service."

But these horsey ones were equal to the vicar. They'd come for a repeat performance of their horseman's Sunday service. They'd come to raise the roof with our choir, singing hymns that they remembered from early days at a service that came back to them with a comforting familiarity.

They are still coming. Some of them are on the church council now, some have joined the choir and gleefully add to the joyful racket kicked up each Sunday. And the parish is now preparing for its first ever horseman's service. There's tremendous interest and no-one at all has complained at the idea of closing the church car park on the day so that they can get the horses in. Alf and the rubbishing bass (who hasn't been heard to say rubbish for some time) are arranging for the local brewery to bring a four horse dray and the decorative soprano has a bewildering number of offers of a ride to church in a variety of most attractive equipages . . . .

SOMETHING FOR EVERYONE

MY friend Sid's village church choir is not what you'd call professional; it's just very enthusiastic and cheerful - and, according to the vicar, whose personal musical world is all plainchant and unaccompanied Mediaeval murmurings, somewhat boisterous. Indeed, in his more desperate moments, in the company only of two or three trusted churchwardens, after having endured one of the choir's thunderous festival choral Evensongs, the vicar has been known to describe it as a prime example of brute force and ignorance.

Unusually, the other evening at choir practice, which Sid has conducted for the past forty years, he was explaining to the girl sopranos what he meant by singing softly. "When I say S-O-R-F-T", he clarified, "I don't mean stop altogether. I mean just calm down a bit so that we can get a contrast with the really beefy bit on the last page of the anthem. You can really let it go then".

A little nut-brown man hardly taller than the vestry piano, he peered affectionately over his half-glasses at his dozen loyal supporters whose ages ranged from eight to eighty. He turned to an outsized youth who, until a few months ago, had shrieked treble in the front row and whose voice, having lately broken, was now hooting a wild kind of alto in the back row. "You're a big lad now", said Sid, "and you've got a very big voice. That's fine, but just keep it down a bit. We don't want it a yard wide when you're standing right next to the vicar on Sunday. He's never been very musical . . . he doesn't appreciate . . . and we don't want any trouble".

Sid likes good sturdy singing and he plays the organ in a

good sturdy way too. In fact, he plays it so sturdily that even a chorister without confidence and who doesn't know the music is encouraged to sing in a gloriously uninhibited manner.

Within living memory the congregation have always enjoyed their music dispensed in this manner - indeed, one could say revelled in it - and although, over the years, a succession of vicars has weighed in with their own ideas, all of which differed widely from those of Sid's choir no one has ever made the slightest impression and all have soon come to realise the truth of the saying "If you can't beat 'em, join em" - even to the extreme extent of accompanying the choir on their annual summer outing to some coastal resort selected for its preponderance of pubs and fun fairs.

It was after the latest of these outings that the emergency arose. It had been noted that during the outward journey the vicar had sat at the back of the coach, looking even more bewildered and dejected than he usually appeared on such occasions, and had closed his eyes and sighed even more often. At the resort he only picked at his fish and chips and, on the homeward journey, refused potato crisps, chocolates and canned beer, and joined in the tumultuous choruses hardly at all. When the party arrived back in the village he had assured everyone how much - indeed, how *very* much - he had enjoyed the splendid day and had disappeared up the vicarage drive before anyone else could struggle out of the coach. The next morning, Sunday, he had reported sick.

And now the hour of Sunday Matins was approaching and there was no one to conduct it. Even the local retired priest was not available, having gone fishing with the latest Ruth Rendell and a large steak and kidney pie.

Members of the choir and some churchwardens and sidesmen stood around in the churchyard assessing the situation. "Anyone can conduct Matins", said a cheerful-looking little man, who had recently come to live in the village. "It's not like communion, where you need a priest. In the parish where I was

13

in London, we used to have all kinds of people taking Matins - our local doctor, the captain of the bellringers, the mayor - just anybody - women . . . it didn't matter at all.

As the others heard these words, there was a frozen silence. Then Sid put things right. "Well, we're not having just anybody taking our Matins", he declared, and there was a visible relaxing of tension. It relaxed even further when one of Sid's tenors, who ran the local garage and possessed some kind of magic that transformed written-off car wrecks into going concerns, said "There's this parson who's on holiday and had a bit of an accident with his car - smashed it to bits down a dyke. I fixed it for him and he's collecting it at half-past nine. He might do".

Half the parish were down at the tenor's garage to look over the man who might do. He arrived on time and certainly would do. He was so excited and delighted at the way his wreck had been transformed ("Looks better than I've ever seen it") that he was indeed eager to oblige in any way he could. He was a big, middle-aged, humorous-looking man who asked to be called Ted, and he kept on circling his little car and patting it and sighing gustily and repeating "Matins at eleven o'clock? Yes, certainly, wonderful, wonderful" - although whether he meant Matins was wonderful or the job on his car was not quite certain.

The little car was given a place of honour outside the lych gate, a place normally reserved for Sid's motor bike, and the beaming volunteer was escorted into the church and given details of the service procedure. His delight grew. "This is a marvellous place", he exclaimed, still unable to remove completely his gaze from his restored four-wheeled friend to be clearly seen through the west doorway. "Everything out of the Prayer Book, it seems, and good old Ancient and Modern. No special do-it-yourself service on a leaflet. No extra 'songs' on bits of paper - and my old travelling companion brought back from the dead. What more can a man ask? What a delightful place".

He possessed a huge basso profundo voice and was a worthy addition to Sid's choir; when he went into the pulpit he had no need of the church's faltering relay system. He said how lucky we were to belong to the Church of England where, these days, members can find almost any kind of service they can imagine, from meditation to dancing in the aisles. He said the goings-on in the last church he had visited, for instance, were rather different from those he was now enjoying. He had had a most enlightening experience in southern England.

Apparently the vicar of the church explained for the sake of first-time attenders that he firmly believed that hymns could not be sung meaningfully unless the words were accompanied by joyous action. Ted was supplied with a booklet of special hymns which the vicar said were relevant praise for today and which consisted of a line or so of basic words repeated three or four

The Vicar kept bawling "Come on raise the roof!"

times for each verse. And while you yelled these out - the vicar kept on bawling "Come on, raise the roof!" - you had to perform the joyous action by clapping and stamping and whirling round and round and smiling at everyone. Ted said that all around him seemed to be thoroughly enjoying themselves, but the whole thing got him so giddy that by the time they'd reached the sixth verse of the first hymn he was not even sure where he was, let alone who he was smiling at. But everyone was very jolly and, after the service, kept handing him cups of coffee and large sticky biscuits made by someone called Pearl, and numerous leaflets about future happy get-togethers in the church . . .

After they'd seen off their providential vistor, still purring over the miracle of his renewed little car, Sid and some of his choir repaired to the *Raven*, their usual Sunday rendezvous after Matins, where discussion turned on Ted's sermon. "Imagine swivelling round and round and clapping hands in our choirstalls", said Sid. "How could you keep your eye on the music?"

"Most of the time we don't look at the music", confessed the car-restoring tenor, "but swivelling round and round - I wonder why they do that?"

An attractive choirgirl broke off from telling the landlord's outsized Boxer dog what a 'booful boy' he was and said "Rapturous joy. It's supposed to be because of rapturous joy".

"It'd be a very noisy kind of rapturous joy in our choirstalls", said Sid, "what with the hollow wood floors and no carpets on 'em".

"And smiling right through the hymn - it must be hard to smile right through a hymn if you're not used to it", suggested the tenor. "It would need a lot of practice".

"People smile at me all the time", said the attractive choir girl, "lots of them". She patted the huge solidity of 'booful boy'. "Look even he's smiling".

"I don't see what it's got to do with hymn-singing", pursued the tenor. "When I was a choirboy you got it in the neck if you smiled at people when you were supposed to be singing".

16

"Times have changed, I reckon", mused Sid. "Thank goodness they haven't changed here, though. What if our choir had to turn itself into a religious pop group and dance in the aisles?"

"We wouldn't be as bad as that terrible lot that play down at the community centre", said the attractive choirgirl, "but they don't smile - they just pull awful faces".

"I remember my niece telling me about a church where they had to stamp their feet when they sang hymns", recounted the tenor. "She said the trouble was that the kids caught on to the idea in a big way and went on stamping like mad right through the service".

"Anyway, what about the hymns for next Sunday?" asked Sid. "We haven't had 'Rock of Ages' for a long time . . . "

FAITH

WE met quite often on an early morning train to London. We first got into conversation when, to pass the time, we started speculating on why our train was so reluctant to make its way to its destination. It was one of those trains that hang about at each station long after the passengers have alighted and boarded, and then stops for a creaking breather between stations as well. As this procedure continued with dependable regularity the subject became rather stale, our jokes about it repetitive and our empty threats against the railway people, boring, and we turned to other topics of conversation. It transpired that my travelling companion was a chorister at a church only a few miles from mine. He was, he said, the lone male alto, known as Hooter, because the choirmaster said he sang like an owl. My enthusiasm to hear about his choir and his unexpected pleasure in finding someone who understood about stubborn vicars and immovable choirmasters and organists, encouraged him to embark on a regular serial story about the fascinating set-up at his church.

The choir were a constant source of discomfiture to the vicar. Not that they knowingly did anything particularly discomfiting apart from singing very loud anthems with words taken from the more bloodthirsty passages in the Old Testament and rendering the vicar's favourite meditative, devotional hymns in the manner of drinking songs in a Bavarian beer cellar. But many a vicar has to put up with similar situations and generally Christian charity or a sense of the inevitable overcomes any angry urges ("Hardly *sensitive* singing - but their *hearts* are in the right place - so loyal, so 'er *enthusiastic*").

However, the case was rather more difficult for this vicar. He was not a good mixer. Despite years of experience he still found it a strain to circulate in the church hall after the Sunday family service and say meaningful things to all the people consuming coffee and biscuits and complaining about the length of the sermon and the last hymn that nobody had ever heard of. And as for the choir, the very thought of circulating anywhere amongst, or with them, never failed to fill him with dismay. He was a mild, middle-aged confirmed bachelor, who kept bees and was shy of the choir's young women and terrified of the older, larger ones and looked upon all choirboys as the ultimate test of faith. Only with the men of the choir (when they were well away from the choir) did he find himself at ease. It happened that, like him, they were middle-aged and cricket and garden loving. Also they had never put their names forward for membership of the parochial church council or any other committee where people argued with the vicar and asked awkward questions about the church heating system and proposed outlandish ideas for replacing choral Evensong.

The vicar fully understood the choirmen's reason for not joining the parochial church council. The P.C.C. was not his favourite organisation either, but of course he always had to be at the meetings to keep some kind of order and to hustle the members through the agenda by midnight or to attempt the near impossible task of getting everyone to agree on a further date when the unfinished arguing could continue.

Doubtless, in view of my interest in the goings-on at his church, Hooter eventually invited me to visit it one Sunday morning and sing in the choir. It was mid-summer and, he said, as his choirmaster never gave the slightest consideration to the fact that a large number of the choir were on holiday at this time of the year, and still kept putting on great long anthems and complicated settings regardless of whether the choir was only half its normal size or had any idea of the music or not, any help in any voice was most welcome. "We did the Alleluia Chorus

19

last Sunday with six people in the choir" Hooter told me, not without a sort of muted pride. "*Handel's* Alleluia Chorus?" I queried. "Well, yes, that's what it said on the music" confirmed Hooter "but it was mostly *our* Alleluia Chorus. I told our choirmaster afterwards that Handel wouldn't have recognised it and certainly wouldn't have attempted to perform it with the choir we had".

"What did he say to that?" I asked.

"Faith" declared Hooter "He said you had to have faith and then you could move mountains".

"And put on the Alleluia Chorus with six people" I said.

"Well five really" he corrected. "One bloke had forgotten his glasses and couldn't even *see* it".

"Your choirmaster must have a *lot* of faith" I said admiringly.

"Oh, he has" Hooter enthused, "and it pays, you know. I can't remember us ever actually *breaking down*. Whatever mistakes we make we still go on singing - our choirmaster insists on that. It's part of his faith y'see. Then the congregation don't even know we've made any slip-ups. They've got faith too. They believe that what they hear us sing is what we are actually *supposed* to sing".

Full of interest - but only a limited amount of faith that I should find Hooter's church (I can lose my way with the greatest of ease crossing the road in unfamiliar territory) I arrived one fine Sunday in August in what I hoped was the right vicinity in plenty of time for morning service. I'm sure that a century ago I'd have spotted the red brick Victorian edifice at once, dominating the high street. Now, however, there was no sign of it in the concrete confusion of supermarkets and high rise office blocks and, it seemed, no one to ask the way. I looked down one or two side streets and studied various signs fixed to lamp posts which gave quite a lot of information about the high street bus stop being moved to the railway station, the quickest way to the crematorium and what would happen to you if your dog misbehaved itself on the cracked, rubbish strewn pavements.

20

But there was nothing about the whereabouts of red brick Victorian churches.

And then appeared a most welcome sight - a man with a Boxer dog who, like all Boxer dogs, appeared to be grinning from ear to ear and, like all Boxer dogs, had a tiny stump of a tail that wagged with such joyous enthusiasm that it convulsed the whole dog. The two of them were on their way to church and were very friendly, particularly the Boxer dog who nearly knocked me over in a frenzy of delight. The man was a churchwarden and the Boxer had his own seat in the corner of the back pew where apparently he was very well behaved during the service - unless the sermon tended to ramble on beyond a reasonable point whereupon he would rise, stretch and utter a very loud yawn.

a Boxer dog . . . grinning from ear to ear

The churchwarden conducted me to the choir vestry which was an unsuspected place behind the organ, full of flower vases and large cardboard boxes containing what looked like rejected jumble sale merchandise. Hooter and the choirmaster stood by a battered piano contemplating the score of a splendid boisterous festival anthem by Goss of the type that, in its heyday was sung at the Crystal Palace by choirs of hundreds. Hooter introduced me to the choirmaster who remarked "Well, that's one more, then. That means we have a choir of six".

"Ah" I said uncertainly.

"That's fine" said the choirmaster, "I'll do the bass solo and we'll do the quartet and other solo bits full choir. Right! Fine!" He had a firm no nonsense manner and his superior dark suit fitted him like a dress uniform.

A decorative soprano was arranging her appearance before a spotty mirror. "You'll sing contralto in the Goss" ordered the choirmaster. "Flavia's got hay fever".

"Right" said the decorative soprano. "Do I know the Goss?"

"You weren't at choir practice Friday night" accused the choirmaster.

"I was chasing the vicar" said the decorative soprano.

"Typical" said the choirmaster.

"I spotted him in the supermarket" explained the decorative soprano. "I'd been trying to get hold of him all the week to ask him if we could have the spring fashion show in the vicarage garden next year but you know what he's like - always out or on the phone"

"I bet he is when he sees you coming" observed the choirmaster. "He saw me and dodged round behind the frozen fish" recounted the decorative soprano "but I cornered him and he started blushing and stuttering and I got him to lend us the garden *and* promise to open the show. It took me ages though. So I didn't get to practice".

"Good heavens!" gasped the choirmaster. "Do you *really* imagine he'll actually do it?"

22

"It's like you are always saying about the choir". She beamed a bewitching smile as the choirmaster. "You've got to have faith".

Well, Sir John Goss would, I am sure, have appreciated the faith our semi-demolished choir had to have to get through his splendid anthem that we sang that evening - "The Wilderness" it was called. Goss, a distinguished nineteenth century organist of St. Paul's Cathedral had to have the same faith to a much greater degree in order to produce the required music from the ramshackle crowd that in his day were known as the Cathedral choir. Sir John would have been pleased with us, I think. We didn't break down.

Faith was strong in the air. I learned some months later from Hooter that even the vicar found some. The decorative soprano *did* make sure that he opened the spring fashion show and to his surprise he enjoyed himself so much being consulted on his fashion ideas by so many charming people that he had put himself forward to open the next year's show. And he finds that chatting over coffee after Sunday morning service is much easier for him now. Not that he approaches it with unqualified enthusiasm even now, for whereas the fashion show people politely, indeed charmingly, asked his opinions, the church crowd pin him in corners before he can even get to the coffee counter and tell him they don't agree with him and what they are going to do about it. Still, it's a beginning and, as the choirmaster says, "You've got to have faith and then you can move mountains".

THE ALLOTTED SPAN

THE choir of the village church where my friend Ernie sings all the tenor solos because he is the only tenor they've got, are firm favourites of their vicar. He particularly appreciates the men of the choir. They all have vegetable and flower allotments just outside the parish where they meet regularly on Saturdays amid the sheds and water butts to talk sport and play cards, and when the allotments begin to look rather too neglected they pull up a few weeds and tie up an occasional sagging bean frame or riotous clump of Michaelmas daisies. And although the vicar has no allotment it is a tradition that he is generally around too.

The organist also has an allotment here which presents itself as a kind of small natural lawn composed of self-sown grass, buttercups and dandelions in a cushion of undisturbed weeds. Here, in a red and white striped deck chair, he presides on warm summer Saturdays (in shed if wet) surrounded by the choir men and here all important decisions about the choir - such as why they shouldn't try out a new 'praise song' suggested by the vicar's warden and which pub to use for the next diocesan choir darts contest - are taken.

When I made a recent visit to Ernie he took me with him to one of these allotment conferences. The choir men sat about on the organist's lawn on various upturned boxes, a milking stool and a wheel-barrow which had no wheel. My seat was an old car seat garlanded with uninhibited raspberry canes and the vicar, beaming and relaxed sat cross-legged in a comfortable clump of dock grass. The charge on the 'committee' on this occasion was the arranging of a special celebration party to mark the sixty years' service in the choir recently attained by The Oldest Member. Preparations for the function had been

24

kept secret from him and it was intended to spring it on him the next Sunday. A large bass gentleman sought to balance himself more securely on the milking stool. "Seeing as how we can't ask him what music he'd like for Evensong on his Sunday, it's a bit difficult to know what he'd like" he proffered profoundly.

"We *know* what he'd like" said the organist - "anything that he knows the tune of so that he can really let rip."

"He does that even when he *doesn't* know the tune" put in a tall thin alto folded in the mossy depths of the wheel-barrow.

"Anyway," posed the organist "What about the presentation - what shall we give him?".

On cue everybody looked attentive and thoughtful. This was the question that always opened the age old obligatory routine preceding a long-service award. The committee would put forward various suggestions and seriously mull them over for exactly ten minutes. It didn't matter what the suggestion was as long as you showed interest by saying *something*, because you knew that it wouldn't be accepted. It was a revered tradition that when your time came for a long-service award you always got a chiming wall clock. Over the centuries dozens of such clocks had been awarded and no one saw the slightest reason why dozens more should not be awarded in the future.

But, as with everything else to do with the choir, a traditional routine had to be followed.

"Socks," boomed the bass balancing on the milking stool, "lots of socks. He likes walking doesn't he? Goes miles a day with his dogs and he wears holes in his socks all the time - he's always on about it. And there's that story that his wife has never mended any of them - throws them away."

"He gets holes in his socks because his boots are too big" said the wheel-barrow alto. "I've *told* him about it."

"What about a couple of pairs of the *right* sized boots then?" suggested another member. "They would stop the holes and look like a better present."

25

"We could give him a lawn mower," said the organist who always said "we could give him a lawn mower" on these occasions. Everyone nodded and looked even more attentive and thoughtful. "I could ask him for mine back then" mused the organist, "he's had it for two years."

"I think a real nice leather-bound copy of 'Messiah' would be a good idea," declared Ernie, reclining meditatively between the shafts of the alto's wheel-barrow.

"Or 'The Damnation of Faust'" supplemented the big bass. "he's always going up to Town to the opera."

"I think he goes to see Gilbert and Sullivan" said the organist. "I don't think he knows anything about 'The Damnation of Faust'".

There was a deep silence. The attentive thoughtful expressions intensified even farther. The alto unfolded himself from the wheel-barrow. "I've got it" he exclaimed. "Why not treat him to a weekend in Paris - all expenses paid for two?" Someone made a violent choking noise. Time for discussion was up. "I know *exactly* what he'd like" announced the organist - "a chiming wall clock - that's the very thing".

Everyone relaxed. "Of course. perfect" they chimed in, "A chiming wall clock."

The presentation party was splendidly organised by the vicar's warden who, despite having his regular request for a favourite praise song totally ignored by the organist, was a great champion of the choir. Nothing would have made him happier than to be in the choir but being tone-deaf he realised that it would not be a very commendable idea. He did, however, have a young son of around four years old who, he felt sure, was destined for greatness in the musical world. Even at this early age, his father announced constantly to all who would listen, he was absolutely terrific on his set of drums, and recently Young Marvel, as his father now exclusively referred to him, had proved himself an absolute virtuoso on mouth organ. He had been given a double sided mouth organ on Christmas Day

one of those allotment conferences

and, so determined was he to master the instrument, that he blew it almost non-stop throughout the whole of Christmas Day and Boxing Day. His father said proudly that it made him think of the surprise and excitement that must have been felt by those privileged to first hear the child Mozart playing the organ. He was sure that the neighbours must have experienced much the same feelings when they heard Young Marvel on the mouth organ.

And now, announced father, Young Marvel would have his very first public engagement - at their presentation party.

On the Sunday evening of the presentation the church hall was early crammed with the entire regular congregation and dozens of people who hadn't heard the choir sing since their wedding services or when they'd rallied round for grandfather's funeral. The scene inwardly shattered the vicar, an incurably shy man who found it tedious to deal with gatherings any bigger that the choir committee and despite his calling, was more at ease with books and flowers. He'd entered the hall unobtrusively via the kitchen. He searched desperately and unsuccessfully for a quiet corner where, hopefully, he could engage a choirman in prolonged conversation and avoid everyone else until such time as a decent escape could be made with a minimum of hand shakes and encounters with people who wanted to know what he was getting at in his sermaon at Matins last Sunday. The vicar was out of luck. As he edged into the hall, he was propelled firmly to the centre of the floor where, on a marble topped pub table, stood the latest chiming clock tied up with yards of yellow ribbon. And next to it, tightly blue suited with glowing white shirt, gleaming black boots and the shining, smooth red face of an ancient cherub, stood The Oldest Member. His wife moved around him frowing and removing invisible foreign specks from his suit. Normally, if they were meeting on the allotment, the vicar and The Oldest Member would have immediately fallen into animated conversation about cricket, or real ale, or ferrets and bees. But now, the sight of his friend wearing a suit, and with his wife, increased the vicar's unease so that he reverted to his usual responses to new members of the congregation who tended to shake hands with him in the church porch after their first service and recount their life histories and how they had managed to end up in this particular village. "Great, Splendid, Jolly good" he exclaimed. "Yes indeed" and turning a frantic smile on The Oldest Member's wife, backed well out of the way as the organist came forward to make the presentation. Suddenly realising the main event was at hand rather earlier than they had expected, some of the ladies behind the trestle tables full of empty glasses started sloshing white wine into and around them at a great rate until everyone held a dripping glass ready for the toast.

Reading from the identical script he had used for the last three choir presentations the organist said how good it was to be here tonight to celebrate Albert's 'er beg pardon, George's attaining a magnificent sixty years' service in the choir. His splendid tenor voice had been a wonderful mainstay and he was sure it would remain so for many years to come. His colleagues felt that a chiming wall clock was most appropriate for one who, throughout all these years, had never been late for a service or practice. A record indeed.

Actually, the latter part of the script didn't really fit The Oldest Member who, being a very rough bass, had never sung tenor splendidly and was always late for services and practices, but no one appeared to notice this and after the toast was drunk the cheering was long and frantic. His wife prodded him and ordered him to say something but luckily everyone had now turned their urgent attention to the side tables loaded with the most appealing savouries and sweets. So The Oldest Member defiantly undid his jacket, loosened his tie and joined them.

And the evening went well. True, the vicar's warden had to waylay the vicar just as he was escaping through the kitchen to inform him that, owing to the sudden indisposition of Young Marvel (he had surreptitiously sampled rather too many mixed savouries and sweets earlier in the evening), there would regretfully be no mouth organ recital. "But don't worry", father had encouraged, "he's agreed to give it at Evensong next Sunday."

"Great, Splendid, Jolly good," stuttered the vicar increasing his stride rapidly. "I'm sure the choir and organist will . . . Oh dear! . . . "

WE SHALL NOT BE MOVED

THEY don't like change at the village church in a secret part of Wiltshire where my cousin George sings in the choir. (It's secret because British Rail have never heard of it and no bus can seem to find its way there even once a week.) Everybody and everything at the church has been there, the same, for at least forty years - except the present vicar. He has been there for only ten years and so is always referred to as the New Vicar; his predecessor who held the post for the regulation forty years is still naturally talked of as the Vicar.

"We have a bit of trouble with the New Vicar now and again" George explained to me one evening during a short holiday I was spending with him in the village. "He has these funny ideas about altering things but the Church Council soon puts him right - and of course, like so many of these new men, he often has go at the choir - says we sing too much Victorian music and why don't we sometimes sing some of the nice modern hymns so much more relevant to today's vital thinking in the church which he has gummed into the front of our 'Ancient and Moderns'. George says that the organist, a splendidly flamboyant octogenarian who still wears spats on Sundays and has a large picture of Wagner pinned up over the organ console, refuses to have anything to do with these hymns because he reckons that you can't tell whether they're relevant to today's vital thinking or not as they all seem to consist of one line repeated three times followed by a chorus of one word repeated four times.

The New Vicar thinks that the organist and the choir are biased. Certainly, he suffers a lot from the activities of the choir.

No matter how kindly and diplomatically he admonishes them (and he is a very kindly and diplomatic young man) the choir still keeps on singing long uproarious Victorian anthems that absolutely shatter his nerves and addle his thoughts on higher things. In desperation he once suggested that the choir should sing an entire service of modern meaningful music just once a quarter but the Church Council turned the idea down flat so the New Vicar carries on suffering.

Each time I visit George and arrive in the vestry as a guest in the choir the New Vicar dutifully bears down on me and shakes my hand and says things like "Well, well, so here we are again. So nice to have you with us to help swell the joyful sound." But on this particular Sunday morning he was looking positively thrilled and beaming at everybody, even the organist. George explained that this was because, just before my arrival, he had heard that the only alto in the choir had suddenly succumbed to 'flu and consequently it would not be possible to perform the anthem. Alas, how short lived can real happiness be! When he realised that I, in fact, sung a sort of alto - till then apparently, what I did in the choir had been a mystery to him - and that the anthem could therefore now go ahead he stoicly held his cheerful smile and said "Good! Splendid! Yes, indeed".

Matins proceeded as a rollicking pace. After an exhilerating streak through the psalms and canticles we roared through a splendid Victorian anthem full of lush duets and rousing bass solos and a final pounding chorus. When we ended in a truly deafening burst of sound - probably rather more deafening than the composer had intended - the New Vicar who has to brace himself to face up to the choir's singing of even a quiet Victorian anthem and is given to humming some of his favourite 'simple, beautiful new hymns' during other people's sermons, took quite a few moments to recover sufficiently to breath "Let us pray". But so upset was he that he started intoning well remembered prayers from the Book of

Common Prayer instead of the modern language prayers he had managed against great odds to slip into the services and which constituted his single victory over the Church Council in ten years. The realisation of the awful reactionary thing he had done flustered him still further and he announced the wrong hymn. Nobody took any notice of him and we all sang the right hymn which was all about golden cities and celestial choirs and people in white robes and harps. The organist plainly enjoyed this so much that he completely drowned out the choir and the congregation - who were singing in a magnificent football crowd unison - in the last verse and easily obliterated the squeaking of the New Vicar's white and grey gym shoes on the polished black and orange Victorian tiles as he made his way to the pulpit.

I'm not quite sure what the sermon was about. I think it was something to do with the Vicar's plans for taking out all the church pews to make the space more flexible for special events such as a motor cyclists' service (including the motor cycles) which he was thinking of arranging to attract the younger element in the parish. But my attention was somewhat distracted by two choirmen next to me who were having an enthusiastic conversation about a steam traction engine rally they were going to on Easter Monday. And as I am infinitely more fascinated by steam traction engines than by motor bikes I'm afraid I didn't follow the sermon beyond the removal of the pews, although George did assure me afterwards that of course the pews would not be removed. The New Vicar, he said, conceived sweeping ideas in rapid succession and his enthusiasm for each new inspiration was so concentrated that he immediately forgot all about the previous one. So there was never much cause for alarm and everyone carried on quite happily.

Anyway, we eventually came to the last hymn during the singing of which a forbidding military moustached gentleman in a black suit thrust a large brass collection plate around the congregation at a tremendous speed while the organist seemed to be increasing the tempo of the hymn at every line. Indeed, I was becoming quite breathless. I subsequently learnt from George that this was all part of a revered tradition in which the choir tried to finish the hymn before the sidesman could get the collection up to the Vicar, and in turn the sidesman endeavoured to pip the choir at the post by delivering the collection before the choir reached the last verse. In this instance the sidesman won handsomely and obviously the victory meant a great deal to him by the way his forbidding expression melted into one of real Christian joy as he winked largely at his rivals.

After the service, to the accompaniment of a thunderous organ voluntary which the organist had cobbled together from "The Twilight of the Gods", the congregation filed out through the elegant west doorway into the immaculate churchyard in a leisurely and dignified manner and the New Vicar started shaking hands with everyone in a most friendly guise.

Astride the famous bike, the organist waved

At the back of the choir vestry the choir shoved out through a battered doorway discreetly hidden behind an exuberant mass of stinging nettles, dead flowers and broken dustbins and nobody shook hands in a friendly or any other way. "Great service, that" pronounced George as we picked our way through the dustbins. "Something you could really get your teeth into".

A grinding noise came from behind us and the organist hailed us pushing the vintage bicycle which was one of the well known sights of the village. It was said that he got it for ten shillings and a set of cigarette cards before the Second World War and that on dark nights he still used its original oil lamp. He repeated warm thanks to me for stepping into the breach and on learning that I'd also be coming to Evensong he said gleefully that we could repeat the anthem. He'd mention it to the New Vicar. . .

At the church door the New Vicar was till shaking hands with the departing congregation (including one enthusiastic little lady who kept on shaking hands and then going to the back of the queue to shake hands again) and enduring the many compliments paid to the choir about 'the really lovely anthem'. He beamed and desperately looked forward to the quiet of his study where as usual on Sunday afternoon he would recover from the effects of Matins by immersing himself in the writings of the new suffragan bishop who was very forward thinking and appeared as often as possible in jeans and a T-shirt.

From the direction of the choir vestry the familiar rattling sound came nearer. Astride the famous bike the organist waved to the New Vicar and unbelievingly the New Vicar heard himself calling our "Splendid effort with the anthem". But the organist was not riding as he normally did. He had turned his bike towards the New Vicar. "Ah, Vicar," he said, grinding to a halt. "About Evensong tonight . . ."

THE CHURCH MUST ADVERTISE

RECENTLY, when I was a guest in the choir of a cheerful-looking battered, hard-up, red brick, late Victorian church in a most unfashionable part of outer London where my friend Jake is organist and choirmaster, the new vicar - a sort of middle-aged dynamo with pronounced theatrical leanings - used choral Matins to put forward his ideas for a church witness event which would be in the form of a float in the town's forthcoming annual May Fair procession. For years the May Fair, organised by the local churches, had been held on the first Saturday in May on the town's permanently vandalised recreation ground and had been traditionally opened with, to quote the posters, "a giant decorated carnival procession" that comprised an elderly council van hung about with paper streamers and six balloons, some members of the local dramatic society wearing outsize paper-mache heads and big boots, a pensioned off diesel road-roller covered in vegetables, a man with a tin whistle and the two or three town councillors (in full dress) who could be persuaded to get out of bed before ten o'clock on a Saturday morning.

Like the majority of the town councillors, the bulk of the population didn't see any reason to rise before ten o'clock on a Saturday even on May Fair day, so the volume of support along the processional route was normally thin to non-existent, and in any case the procession got so strung out and merged in the through traffic along the main road that it had always completely disappeared long before it could reach the fair ground.

The big crowds did materialise, however, some two hours

35

later when the central point of the proceedings, the colossal beer tent, was opened and its satellite "antique" and "fashion" stalls had been loaded with tons of rubbish specially culled from attics, garages and garden sheds for miles around. The weather always seemed to be fine and the crowds always increased to frightening proportions and drank all the beer and purchased all the rubbish, and everyone went home and pronounced the fair another great success.

But the opening procession remained a sad, lonely, almost unknown outcast. And the new vicar had decided to do something about it. So on this Sunday morning he strode up and down the aisle faster and faster as his inspirations for the church float tumbled over each other. "You see, the church has got to advertise", he enthused. "We must be seen to be believed". He has a way of emphasising a point by suddenly pointing to someone and holding the stance in perfect silence for a number of seconds before shouting, "Imagine! Just imagine . . ."

This time he swung round and targeted our bass soloist who was dozing gently in the choir stalls. "Imagine - just imagine", he commanded, "What would be the wonderful outcome if everyone in town knew of the joy and fellowship of our Sunday mornings in this church". Nobody else in the choir noticed what the vicar was doing so nobody wakened the bass soloist to imagine the joy and fellowship, and the vicar moved on regardless, saying, "Yes - quite right - our church would be bursting at the seams - packed to the rafters".

He then explained that he'd been able to arrange the loan of a builder's lorry and now invited the congregation to form a working party to get down to producing a church float that would be the talk of the town. "Volunteers now", he beamed, pointing dramatically to various persons and repeating, "Jolly good, splendid", before they had time to think of declining. "A meeting in the vestry after Evensong tonight will be ideal", he concluded. "All of us with lots of ideas - for something really *spectacular*".

Such was the glowing persuasive power of the man that a large number of us who had not been actually nominated as volunteers found ourselves crowded into the vestry with the chosen ones after Evensong, where attendance had been at least twice the normal size. He didn't waste time. He opened the meeting by calling immediately for suggestions but, even before he could point to the first volunteer, the Any Other Business man was on his feet and in full flood. The AOB man, a huge tweed-clad character with a figure like an all-in wrestler, had been on the church council for ages and had earned his title from his unfailing habit of having absolutely nothing to say throughout the entire meeting until late into the night, all the other members having got thoroughly fed up with arguing with each other and getting nowhere, the last item on the agenda, Any Other Business, had been reached. The AOB man would then rise like a prophet of old, fix his gaze firmly above the chairman's head on to a clock with one hand and, using the language of some of his best-loved Victorian hymns, would urge that the church must march as to war and smite its enemies and slay evil-doers. This would go on until the chairman could slip in a firm and final expression of thanks for "those inspiring and indeed much-needed words" and quickly intone the closing prayer.

But at this meeting the AOB man had caught everyone napping. Far from bringing up the rear, he had led the attack. Our float must portray fearless Christian warriors, he declared, vanquishing dragons and evil hordes - and things like that. "Charge for the God of battles!" he finished triumphantly.

The vicar said, "Yes, thank you indeed", and a little lady with a surprisingly commanding voice suggested that friendship and helpfulness should be the theme, and that we should have a float full of teenagers doing things like helping old people cross roads and cleaning risque grafiti from walls. Her suggestions were followed by a number of others involving healthy eating and drinking and exercise, and one which called for the choir to appear on the float wearing their new plum-coloured cassocks ("Such a lovely *shade*") and handing out free surplus parish magazines.

A group of highly respected, long -service parishioners, who had always agreed fervently with the views and doings of the old vicar, and now did the same with the new vicar although the outlooks of the two vicars were quite at variance, were very keen that the vicar should appear as St. Francis of Assissi.

Jake, who is of a somewhat cynical nature, having dealt intimately with vicars, parochial church councils, and church choirs over many years, summed up by congratulating the gathering on really getting to grips with the subject. "I can see our float now - clearly!" he exclaimed excitedly "All those incredibly heroic warriors smiting and slaying all over the

"Imagine! Just imagine . . .

place, while helpful young people are scrubbing the walls and helping old people across the road to the health club where everybody is doing exercises like mad against a background of lovely plum-coloured cassocks and St. Francis is chatting with the animals and birds because everyone else is too busy or frantic to talk to him . . . "

The vicar thanked Jake for his "usual and much-enjoyed comic relief" and finally someone had a good idea. It was decided to delay the May Fair procession until more of the customers had got out of bed, so it started at mid-day. The vicar's builder's lorry failed to materialise, as did a definite theme for the church float, but at the last moment the local brewery came forward with the offer of a horse-drawn dray. The name of the church was strung up above the name of the brewery and the dray hastily loaded with gleeful-looking parishioners who were ticked pink with the idea of substituting for barrels of beer. And the four champion Shire horses that drew the dray also drew by far the most enthusiastic attention from the crowds who surrounded them with batteries of cameras and small children.

There is little that escapes the new vicar's eye when it comes to ideas for filling the pews. He has now taken down the NO DOGS notice in the churchyard and is urgently planning the next great church witness event - a monster animal blessing service. He has already arranged for the choir to arrive in their new plum-coloured cassocks on the brewery horse dray . . .

THE SCREEN

THE Suffolk village church where I am sometimes a guest in the choir is a Mediaeval gem. It is also extremely decrepit and over the last two hundred years has been regularly saved from complete collapse by the same highly respected firm of local builders who are ever ready to bodge it up as each desperate emergency arises. Towards the end of the nineteenth century they put up a flamboyant chancel screen given by a lady who sat in the middle of the front row and was fed up with always having to look at the choirboys' dirty knees which were clearly visible through the open work choir stalls and buttonless cassocks. The church council of the day were very pleased to accept the screen because not only did it hide the dirty knees - it also made it less likely that the venerable and ailing chancel arch would one day fall down all over the choir.

But the present-day new vicar, a worshipper of all things Mediaeval, knew nothing of the history or the practical value of the screen and only saw what he described to a few like-minded cronies as a vulgar Victorian monstrosity. Indeed, after only a few months in the parish his horror of the brutal desecration of the Mediaeval gem had grown to an all-out obsession that drove all other parish matters from his mind.

The very word 'Victorian' had always made him shudder. In other parishes where he had served he had constantly to brace himself in face of Philistine choirs and congregation who were ever wanting to sing dreadful gushing Victorian hymns with tunes that seemed to have come straight from the music-hall or a smoking concert. He had had to deal with awful parishioners who insisted on retaining and preserving Victorian churchyards crammed with gravestones full of verses about people being gone but not forgotten and singing in celestial choirs. He had even been inveigled into heading a parochial church council committee organising a scheme for the restoration of a monstrous red and green Victorian stained glass window depicting St. George getting the better of the dragon.

And now, the church screen was the last straw. The new vicar decided to fight. He started to put out feelers. How would people like it if the very splendid view of the Mediaeval chancel was fully revealed again, unimpeded by the gross bulk of the Victorian screen? The response from the congregation was meagre. Either they had never realised the Mediaeval splendours of the chancel or they thought that the chancel screen was quite nice. Certainly, few thought it should be removed and most didn't appear to think at all. Only the choir had a firm and unanimous opinion. They were outraged at the idea.

On the bottom panels of the screen were numerous brass memorial tablets to choristers who had sung in the choir for years and years. What would happen to them if the screen were to be removed? And what would happen to the marrows and cabbages and bags of tomatoes and bundles of onions that were always hung all over the screen at harvest festival? Besides, how could members of the choir carry on reading their Sunday papers and doing things they traditionally did during the sermon if the screen was pulled down to reveal their every moment to the congregation? The whole crazy idea was out of the question.

All this I learned from a letter from the organist who is an old school friend of mine who had invited me to the village for the weekend of the local horse show. Shire horses being great favourites of mine together with trams, paddle steamers and the earlier editions of 'Hymns Ancient and Modern'. So now, eager to admire the horses and enjoy a good uninhibited sing in the village choir I'd arrived in the village.

41

Discussing the Victorian chancel screen question with my friend the organist over supper it was evident that he was regarding the whole thing very philosophically. After all, as he pointed out, there were always people these days who were anxious to change things and upset the apple cart. A year ago, for instance, there had been trouble with the 'Rip-out-the-Victorian pews' brigade who wanted to replace the pews with those little wooden chairs, presumably made for midgets, where there is nowhere to put your hymn book and when you kneel down your heels get trapped under a bar of the chair behind.

Then there were some very persistent women who wanted to turn the churchyard into a kiddies' playground with goldfish ponds and sections of concrete sewer pipes to crawl through and a skate board track all round the church.

There was also a pressure group who felt that the church should be more prominent in the neighbourhood and wanted to frame the notice boards and the tower clock with red and blue neon tubes, but no one took any notice of them because they mainly belonged to the crowd who persisted in coming to Sunday Evensong instead of the Family Communion service and were regarded by the vicar very much as third-class citizens.

"But, not to worry," my friend leaned back in his comfortable, although I always think, disreputable, old armchair and stretched his legs towards the fire. His tone was unperturbed, reassuring. "The vicar's just doing his 'new broom' act - all new vicars do. He'll never get the screen taken out. We'd have to get a faculty and they'd be meetings, arguments, alternative suggestions, letters to the local paper and people resigning from the choir and the flower committee. Probably, some important character, organising a rally in the churchyard before Matins or a sit-down strike in front of the screen at Evensong, would drop dead and we'd all be back where we started - no the vicar'll never get that screen thrown out.

The next day my friend and I arrived early at church for Sunday Matins to find the vicar apparently driving a small,

cheerful Victorian splendour

middle-aged rather startled looking man up and down the aisle in a most relentless manner. The vicar was in full flood and appeared to be reaching a climax of fiery exaltation to the little man to behold and marvel at the glories of his Mediaeval surroundings. As we approached he towered over his victim and demanded, "Have you ever seen anything so inspiring in a mere village church - badly treated by time but still so superb, so pure - "He raised his hands dramatically towards the roof and held a brief silence. The little man grabbed his chance.

"My grandfather sang in the choir here for sixty years" he piped. "I believe there is a memorial to him somewhere in the church. Can you show me? Name of Hodge. I want to take a photograph. I'm on holiday from New Zealand." The vicar slowly lowered his arms. He looked bewildered, as if he didn't know were he was. My friend stepped forward, "Let me show you," he invited the little man. We all gathered at one end of the chancel screen at the foot of which was the memorial to one, Hodge, a mighty Victorian bass, a pillar of the choir cricket team - a great man.

The vicar recovered enough to join us round the plaque. "A splendid record", he murmured and smiled bravely.

"And a splendid place for a memorial to be," responded the little man. "What a lovely screen."

It transpired that the little man sang alto in his church choir in New Zealand, so he joined us in the choir for Matins. He said afterwards he'd never enjoyed a service so much. My friend the organist said he was very pleased to hear it. At the Family Service on Sundays the vicar always had his way with the singing of hymns that were new and meaningful and related to today's vital problems and aspirations and the psalm too was always a modern re-hash which was also meaningful and related. But at Matins the congregation and choir had their way and the vicar, feeling very democratic and forgiving, endured the kind of music that the bass, Hodge, would have thundered out in the 1890s and that the present singers still championed.

New Zealand had been kind to the little man and prospered him and the little man was now kind to his grandfather's church. Before he returned to New Zealand a few days later he handed the vicar a cheque of considerable value. He asked that the money should go towards the restoration of the church - including attention to the screen which seemed to be scarred and knocked about in places.

Eighteen months later he was with us again at a special thankgiving service for the restoration made possible by his generosity. Much good work had been done on the tower and the magnificent nave roof and the chancel arch - and the screen,

44

repolished, regilded, restored to its cheerful Victorian splendour, guarded the choir with a new authority.

The vicar was overjoyed at the results of the unexpected help. He tries to perpetuate his enjoyment by not looking at the newly glittering chancel screen but people keep saying how lovely it is and this makes him rather sad at times but he soon cheers up. Recently a publisher invited him to contribute a key article to a forthcoming, very learned book on Mediaeval church architecture and he is now so busy and delighted and elated that brash Victorian screens and awful Victorian choirs are almost beneath his notice.

TRADITION

MY FRIEND Henry's village church is so historic that, despite being buried in the back of beyond, it yearly draws hundreds of visitors off the beaten track and the church council does a roaring trade selling T-shirts, tea-cloths and key rings bearing a romantic likeness of the church.

The body of the church has an appropriate historic heating system that only the vicar's warden understands and which, nevertheless, the congregation all agree is very efficient and never gives any trouble (no one and nothing under the vicar's warden's eye ever dares give any trouble). But up in the choir they've never really had a heating system at all and in the winter the choir have depended entirely on the odd oil stove here and there and thick pullovers under their choir robes. No one in the choir ever seems to have complained about this and it has been accepted as part of the very historic set-up. However, recently during the summer months, the vicar's warden has been instrumental in having a brand new heating system installed in the choir. A very thorough and determined man, he early on decided that the system should be thoroughly tested in readiness for its winter duties.

Life can be mischievous. The Sunday chosen for the test (a day that coincided with one if my occasional 'guest appearances' in the choir) dawned quite unexpectedly and exceptionally hot for early September - or for any other month for that matter - but the vicar's warden, being so thorough and determined (he is basically a nice man and no one ever calls him stubborn) went ahead operating the new system at full blast. As the choir processed into the chancel from the cob-webbed coolness of their vestry, a wave of tropical heat met us and enveloped us in the choir stalls. No one seemed to take any notice, however, and we started off Matins in our usual rousing manner with one of the vicar's favourite militaristic Victorian hymns all about avenging angel armies and golden cities.

But from then on the fates were against us. The psalm appointed for that particular Sunday was one of the longest and most repetitive in the book and set to one of the only chants we didn't know by heart, the rest of the hymns appeared to have dozens of seemingly endless verses set to dawdling unco-operative tunes and the anthem (unaccompanied) seemed to get longer and longer as we ploughed through it, and more and more tuneless and flatter and flatter until it petered out in a sort of discordant groan.

Following this, the vicar extended the prayers by leaving long gaps for what he called individual meditation and private thought during which the congregation stared about the church and wished he'd get on with it. . Then, in an extra long sermon he went on and on about the laity being the church, not just the clergy. What he seemed to be saying was that he wanted members of the congregation to take over the parish visiting and only bring him into proceedings if some awkward parishioner absolutely insisted on seeing him or threatened to withdraw from the free-will offering scheme.

During the final hymn someone's infant at the back of the church had clearly had enough and started bawling and kicking the pew with astonishing vigour and this encouraged another infant to start kicking another pew with equally astonishing vigour. Those in charge simply smiled proudly at their offspring and went on singing but the uproar upset the organist to such an extent that he played the organ so loudly he not only drowned the infant protest but also drowned the choir who nevertheless carried on in their usual manner, splendidly ignoring the infants, the organ and hot-house heat.

Immediately after the service I went to the back of the

church to speak to a friend in the congregation and returning to the vestry a few minutes later I found a few members of the choir standing around still apparently quite unaffected by the tropically heated Matins we had just sung through. Henry brought me into the conversation. "He's gone off in a huff - said we sang the anthem utterly insensitively - utterly". I knew who he was talking about. Everyone in the choir always refers to the organist as 'he' or 'him' and has quite happily put up with him for years - like they've put up with the lack of heating - as part of the church's unique historical background.

Actually, I thought we'd sung to our usual standard for the Matins anthem but I realised that this particular anthem had been a special request of the vicar's - a brand new work by someone his wife's cousin knew who was apparently a rising young genius destined to go far - and the organist was very impressed by rising young geniuses destined to go far . . .

There was a short silence while we all thought on this strange huffiness of the organist, then a choirgirl who has a delightful soprano voice - and in the eyes of all the male members of the choir is altogether delightful - flung her choir gown over a tarnished brass rail where a confusion of like gowns had already been flung. "I don't know what he's making such a fuss about" she said. "The congregation never listen to the anthem anyway. The front pews were all asleep before we'd finished this morning".

"The vicar said it was a very moving piece of music" remarked a comfortably round tenor gentleman looking up from the headline horror of his Sunday tabloid. "Moving!" repeated the choirgirl "It'd take a jolly sight more than *that* dirge to move our Matins lot. You couldn't move them with a bulldozer. Why, they even go to sleep when the vicar does one of his 'we must all arise and march forward together' sermons and keeps bashing on the pulpit and bawling".

"Well, they're used to it" said Henry. "They know he's not really upset". We moved into the churchyard where some of the congregation lingered to gossip in the shade of the trees rather than gossiping in the terribly hot coffee room with the terrible coffee.

A large, obviously important lady who had slept in the middle of the front pew drifted stately across to the choirgirl. "That *lovely* anthem" she purred. "You all sung it so thrillingly. I was on the edge of my seat *right* through". Nothing discomposed the choirgirl. Captivating hazel eyes sparkled. "Thank you very much" she beamed.

That evening there took place the traditional Choir Benefit Evensong when the whole congregation are supposed to turn up especially to listen to the choir and, in recognition of their devoted service, put a lot of money into the special collection for the choir's annual outing. The Choir Benefit Evensong has taken place on the second Sunday in September from as far back as anyone in the parish can remember. It is the occasion when, according to the vicar's warden, the choir mercilessly slaughter some of the most beautiful church music ever composed and the vicar gets out of preaching the sermon with the excuse that nothing he can say can possibly compensate for taking up time in which the choir could be 'giving such joy with their glorious singing'.

The congregation are nothing if not loyal to tradition and

"That lovely anthem" she purred.

49

dutifully fill the church at each Choir Benefit Evensong and thankfully fill the collection bags when it's at last over and they can escape. Only a few actually find it impossible to face the ordeal but the choir outing fund doesn't suffer because the backsliders always pay generous conscience money.

As usual the latest Choir Benefit Evensong was a resounding success with every pew crammed and a very generous sum in the collection. Not that the choir are ever fooled by the apparent demonstration of appreciation by the congregation. As the organist impressed on me after the service, some of his best friends were members of the congregation and they were all utter philistines quite incapable of recognising beautiful singing. "The only reason why they stick it listening to the choir for over an hour is because of the free 'do' at the vicarage afterwards," he assured me.

Tradition further dictated that, following the Choir Benefit Evensong, the vicar should entertain both choir and congregation at a jolly celebration at the vicarage and the vicar, always grasping another opportunity for a demonstration of parish 'togetherness', had set to work with a will organising a team to produce the trestle tables loaded with tiny sausages on sticks, even tinier sandwiches and 'special offer' supermarket wine so dear to the hearts of church party organisers.

Choir and congregation mingled heart-warmingly in the overflowing vicarage drawing room and remarks like "*wonderful evening*", "really *lovely* singing", "I listened absolutely *riveted*" and "I sometimes wonder what it would be like if we didn't have a choir at all" drifted warmly amongst the genteel crush.

The delightful choirgirl stood near me at the end of a trestle table observing the scene and discreetly consuming three microscopic sandwiches at a time. "What a wonderful thing tradition is" she remarked to me, smiling dazzlingly across the room at the vicar's warden who was trying determinedly to photograph her from the midst of the swaying surge of well-wishers around the 'special offer' wine table.

A *REAL* FAMILY SERVICE

THEY were breaking in a new vicar at the Berkshire village church where my Aunt Rosie sings in the choir. Rosie has been in the choir almost as long as the old vicar, a happy bachelor, had been at the church. And very few people could remember when he hadn't been there. He and his vintage motor cycle and sidecar were part of the very fabric of the village. But now, at an undisclosed advanced age, he'd retired and moved to Derbyshire to join a brother of even more advanced age in his hill climbing activities.

The new vicar, a recently married young man full of enthusiasm and dozens of ideas for radical change in the parish that nobody wanted to know about, was carrying on undaunted, serenely sure that his ideas were right and would therefore eventually succeed. To his sorrow, however, he had to admit that a sizeable portion of the congregation led by the choir had made it quite clear to him that they didn't want to be messed about with any of his 'thrilling new thinking' about Sunday services. They knew exactly what they liked, had always liked and intended to go on liking. It was, for instance, simply no good the vicar going on about introducing his relevant-to-today, meaningful 'praise songs' concerning chummy, caring communities and happy industrial relations to replace favourite Victorian hymns about angel choirs and heavenly Jerusalems.

The vicar was secretly worried about the impression his church was creating in a rapidly changing Anglican world and especially in the neighbouring village church where all was light and joy and hand-shaking and hugging and no-one had ever

51

heard of the Book of Common Prayer. It was all such a great pity, this ignoring of the vicar's wishes. He freely admitted that his congregation were a splendid crowd at bottom, fiercely loyal to the Church, widely active in all good works - generous, cheerful. But when it came to Sunday services, although there were reasonable attendances at the modern Family Service, there was this underlying lot who would insist on carrying on with these awful formal services with yards of four-square psalms and canticles that no-one but the choir could sing - and, of course, the aforesaid hymns about angels and heavenly Jerusalems.

And it was indeed with hymns that the new vicar was most concerned. He had, waiting in the wings, a large paperback volume of new 'praise songs' that he was bursting to introduce into the church services as soon as he could inveigle the choir into looking at it. And the best way to tackle the choir, he thought, was to get really chummy with their most influential member, who was undoubtedly Rosie. Wasting no time in accomplishing this pleasant state he embarked on tactics well known to his kind. From various willing sources in the local post office and pub, he sought to discover Rosie's main interests and pastimes apart from her choir activities. The trouble was that Rosie's only other absorbing interest was cats - she has three huge round identical tabbies who only she can tell apart - while the extent of the new vicar's knowledge about cats was that they were things that dug up his carrots and made a row at night. But, as has been said, he was an undaunted, serenely sure character and he pushed on eagerly with his plan. Every time he waylaid Aunt Rosie in the village street or trapped her in the coffee room after the Sunday morning Family Service he beamed at her and asked how the cats were.

He blundered. Far from producing the required chummy atmosphere between them, this only annoyed her more and more because she was fed up saying "Oh! fine Vicar, just fine" - and this was all she *could* say about them because they were always in the peak of condition and never did anything but loll about all over the place looking magnificent.

Aunt Rosie is, however, a very polite person and her facade of pleasure at the vicar's continuous concern for her cats was flawless. Thus, after a few weeks he considered that the time was ripe to introduce to her the subject of 'praise songs'.

He trod carefully. One Sunday morning at coffee he bounced up to Rosie and asked the usual caring question about her cats but before she could give the usual appreciative answer he said that, just for a bit of variety, didn't she think it would be quite

He bounced up to Rosie

fun for the choir to try out one or two really relevant new hymns (he prided himself on his caution in using the word 'hymns' instead of 'praise songs' - that could come later) from a really lovely book that he had recently come across? Rosie replied that as long as he kept the things *strictly* to the Family Service where everybody seemed to do just what they liked anyway and the chaos altered from week to week, and he didn't start messing up *proper* services like choral Matins and Evensong with them, she was sure the choir couldn't care less. And the cats were fine, just fine, thank you. And the vicar said "Good! Splendid! Grand!" but wasn't quite sure whether he'd scored a point or not.

It was about this time that I paid one of my regrettably infrequent visits to Aunt Rosie. On these occasions the proceedings at her 18th century cottage 'The Cubby Hole' are always cosily familiar. Aunt Rosie produces an abundance of home-made hot buttered scones and a generous pot of beverage that she calls real tea, the like of which I have never been able to produce with London water even with the most exclusive tea bags.

She then looks me up and down, asks if I'm *sure* I'm eating enough and sleeping well and goes on to tell me all that has happened in the village since my last visit. In reality very little does happen - the village doesn't move with the times. Indeed it remains as it was fifty years ago, so Rosie's bulletins are mostly repetitive. But they are never dull. The old vicar used to say that she could make a visit to the village shop for six eggs a sensational story. However, this time there *was* a new topic - an in-depth assessment of the new vicar. Aunt Rosie spoke for minutes in the manner of a form mistress reporting to parents as kindly as she possibly could, on the prospects of a well-below-average pupil. She concluded optimistically "He's as stubborn as any man but I'm sure he *can* be led. In the right hands I don't think he'll be much trouble at all. True, he's got the odd fixation about his book of doggerel - his 'praise songs' - but then *all* vicars have some kind of eccentricity, I find, and we can get round this one easily by agreeing to sing his stuff at the Family Service. It'll probably go well with dancing in the aisles which I'm sure is coming next.

Well, unconventional happenings were already occurring at the new vicar's Family Service and the Sunday of my visit to Aunt Rosie was no exception. As I neared the choir vestry door - I have a standing invitation to join the choir during my visits - two excited little girls with saucer-round eyes scampered into my path and squeaked "There's all lions and tigers in the vestry". And one of them added shrilly "and Helephants!"

"And Helephants!" I gasped. "We must see about this."

And indeed the place was a chaos of roaring, trumpeting choirboys all wearing pantomime animal skins and paper-mache heads. "Our wild life support effort - the whole collection will go to conservation projects" beamed the vicar from the midst of the scrum, and the uproar increased rapidly until the organist, an austere figure, apparelled as always in an immaculate grey pin stripe suit, appeared from nowhere, lifted the heads off two of the most ferocious tigers and explained to them in cultured tones that unless they desisted immediately he would personally eject them to the churchyard from whence they would be utterly precluded from entering into the imminent junketings in the church. He then reminded the rest of the menagerie that they were still required, nay, ordered, to sing throughout the service as human beings. The gentlemen of the choir would, of course, don their usual cassocks and surplices and remain human and do their best to keep things civilised. The vicar said "Great, Splendid" and kept on beaming, the organist disappeared into the organ and we all herded into the church in front of a packed congregation. I didn't see any lions or tigers or elephants amongst them but I did spot a curiously hollow-backed zebra and there was a gorilla handing out the service leaflets whose coat looked like a discarded hearth rug and who wore the highly polished shoes of the retired major who usually took up the collection.

Like the hollow-backed zebra the service had no particular shape as far as I could discern, but we kept on singing things from the vicar's praise song book accompanied by, I think, a buffalo and a sort of crocodile who were beating drums out of time with the choir who were out of time with the organ. Then the vicar ambled up and down the main aisle saying what seemed some very inspiring things although I couldn't hear his actual words because the relay system in the choir stalls had gone wrong and everything sounded like a British Rail station announcement.

Finally we did sing something I recognised - "All Things Bright and Beautiful" - while the collection was taken. There was so much to collect that the gorilla with the shiny shoes had to call on the sort of crocodile to assist him and we sang the last two verses of the hymn again while we waited for them.

Later, safe in the serene orderliness of choral Matins, I reflected on the Family Service Wild Life romp.

The vicar was in ecstasies because the choir had actually used his new praise song book, the wild life societies would certainly be delighted with what was in the gorilla's plate and I was happy indeed that the affair was an occasion, although, sadly, a very rare one, when the Church actually acknowledged that Christians should care, not selfishly only for humankind, but also for the rest of God's creation that shares this world with us and is in our care. That had been a *real* Family Service.

DRESSED FOR CHURCH

THE choir at a favourite church of mine are renowned far and wide for being immaculately turned out with stylish cassocks and gowns and ever crisp gleaming surplices, all supported by shining black shoes.

They haven't always presented this pristine appearance. The transformation came some years ago (before ladies graced the choir, let it be said) when a father of the bride strongly objected to his fairy-tale bedecked daughter being preceded up the aisle by - as he complained to the vicar after the ceremony - 'a bunch of characters who looked as though they'd been outfitted from a discarded clothes stall and had just got the worst of it in a pub brawl'. And he had added that their singing was 'like you might hear from the same pub late on a Saturday night after a rugby final'.

The then vicar had taken immediate, firm action and from that time the choir had unfailingly presented their now famed vision of dress perfection at every service. True, in the matter of singing, the organist, unlike the vicar, had not taken immediate firm action or, indeed, any sort of action at all - he never liked to upset the choir - and there are some members of the congregation who reckon that the bride's father's description of the choir's singing remains very true today.

But the choir are not at all worried about these critics. Thanks to the recent addition of girls into this hitherto all male organisation their number is considerably increased these days and now almost everyone in the congregation has a connection with someone in the choir. And as the latest vicar keeps on drumming into everyone that they are all part of one great happy helping family (the previous vicar who had transformed the choir's appearance would never have dreamed of suggesting such a sensational thing) and likes putting on services where you have to keep on shaking hands and hugging each other it's a bit difficult for anyone to have a go at the choir and still appear happy and helpful.

On a recent warm summer Sunday morning the choir processed into church impressively immaculate, to sing choral Matins. I was with them on one of my all-to-rare visits, looking forward to a pleasant hour singing my favourite hymns and chanting my favourite chants and listening to my favourite sermon. The vicar always preaches basically the same sermon with only surface variations to suit the immediate circumstances. It is a highly entertaining diversion about his experiences as a plumber in the days before his wife got him interested in becoming a priest and thus dispensing with the necessity of having a disreputable van parked on the path across the front door and the task of dealing with an endless flow of unwashable washing.

We moved into the choir stalls with dignified precision and made a splendid colourful picture of uniformity. The organist was quite out of the picture behind a smart blue velvet curtain so no one minded that he had not yet got round to wearing his new cassock and surplice and effected still his original dress of shirt sleeves in summer and darned pullover and scruffy neck scarf in winter. And, to tell the truth, his mode of dress seems far more in sympathy with the spirit of the family service (which precedes Matins at this church) than the faultless formality of the choir's attire.

Amongst the Family Service congregation the idea seems to be to outdo each other in informal garb. There are the usual jeans - both the vaguely presentable and the types which look as though they'd fall to bits if you washed them. There are the summer shorts whose colours put Jacob's coat to shame and footwear that, to say the least of it, is startling and in some cases on a hot summer morning, non-existent. One of the two middle-aged gentlemen who take up the collection generally wears a yellow and red T-shirt emblazoned with the word SMILE and the other sports an off-white affair recommending someone's beer.

On the other hand the Matins congregation all wear well-cut suits and blazers or discretely expensive dresses and footwear. They don't all huddle together like the Family Service supporters but sit about the church in their own little islands looking quietly assured and rather elegant.

The choir like Matins more than the Family Service because at Matins they sing music they never have to practice because they've sung it regularly for years and long before the introduction of the Family Service with its new hymns (firmly called 'praise songs' by the vicar) and its special 'turns' and surprise items slipped in here and there so that people won't become bored. To be fair though, the Family Service praise songs don't really need practising either because you only have to beat time by clapping or stamping and look as though you are enjoying it all and they sing themselves.

And let it be said, the vicar infinitely prefers the Family Service where the praise songs are regularly bawled. In common with many vicars today he equates informality and vacuous verse and music with sincerity of worship and true Christian fellowship. Well-meaning fellow that he undoubtedly is, however, he does play his part at Matins when he can't get anybody else to conduct it and always gives members of the Matins congregation a cheery smile when he thinks he recognises any of them in the street.

At this particular Matins service the choir were indulging themselves with a particularly florid Victorian setting of the Te Deum which disturbed the vicar not a little because there seemed no way you could accompany it by clapping or doing a merry jig. But, as always, he put a brave face on things and grinned encouragingly at some small girl recruits in the choir who were coping with vintage Stainer very well, having first removed their chewing gum and stuck it in the usual place under the book rest.

And so Matins rolled comfortably on its splendid formal way. I enjoyed spotting the subtle alterations to suit the situation that the vicar made in his 'When I was a plumber' sermon and we finished strongly with "Oh Happy band of pilgrims" which we found most invigorating as the organist set such a fast pace on the organ that the pilgrims ended up not merely 'onward treading' but positively bounding.

In the vestry after the service we carefully hung up our gorgeous robes in the appointed place, the vicar in a spirit of true Christian charity thanked us for singing so beautifully such beautiful music and the organist, he of the shirt sleeves and no sense of decorum, emerged from the organ loft and called out "Talk about *hot* up there! Anyone for a pint? - my treat". Two or three of the choir men thought this a good idea and moved off smartly with the organist. An explosive

"Do I look stupid?"

rearguard of choir boys and girls followed and I was left alone in the vestry fiddling with my camera with which I had planned to take some photographs of the interior of the belfry.

Presently, the vicar who had been shaking hands vigorously, indeed violently some called it, with the tail-end of the Matins congregation who had not been quick enough to escape the violence, whirled back through the vestry and as he whirled shouted how grand it was to see me in the choir again and what a pity I'd missed the Family Service as it was particularly jolly this morning. They had a visiting priest, a simply *great* colleague who did some really amazing magic for the children and one of the children's fathers who was a weight lifter had given a demonstration.

"Do I look stupid?" I turned, startled, to be confronted by a large fuming contralto choir lady to whom everyone in the choir showed proper respect at all times and tried to avoid at all costs, particularly when she cornered you and demanded to know if she looked stupid. This was always a prelude to the lady telling you of her latest collision with the vicar, the organist or the entire church council about the shananigans they got up to at the Family Service and expecting your unquestioning support in making the vicar, organist and church council feel thoroughly guilty and unconditionally repentant.

"Do I look stupid?" the lady repeated. I'd never really thought about it. I assured her quickly that I didn't think she looked stupid, and this seemed to make her even more cross. "Just *listen*" she commanded. "I've been insulted - the whole choir have been insulted".

"Ah", I managed.

"It's that *man*" she said.

"The vicar's warden" I hazarded.

"Of course" she hooted - she's that kind of contralto. "He's just spoken to me. He actually expects me to *believe* that the only reason the choir won't be wanted at his daughter's wedding service at Christmas is because there's a choral society

61

at her firm which she conducts and she wants *them* to sing the
special music she's chosen. He says that the decision in no way
reflects unfavourably on the beauty of *our* singing which gives
him so much joy at Matins every Sunday - Balderdash!"

"He does tend to exaggerate" I agreed.

"Exaggerate" she roared. "At the choir dinner last year he
said that fine attire couldn't disguise mediocrity".

"Perhaps he was referring to the bishop" I said - "He was
the guest of honour, wasn't he?"

She glared at me. She tried again. "He doesn't *like* the choir"
she stated simply, her tone suddenly gentle and kindly as of one
trying to enlighten a particular dense infant.

"He doesn't like *anybody*" I said. "He can't stand the Family
Service lot".

A quite unexpected silence followed my words, then the
lady with another change of tone mumbled meditatively, "True,
true. Come to think of it I've often heard him tearing them to
bits. Yes - I suppose he's not so bad really".

From a row of fading sepia photographs on the wall above
our magnificent choir robes half a dozen Victorian vicars gazed
down at us. I wondered what they were thinking.

Printed by Attwood Dawes Printers,
Canon Place, Eskdaill Street, Kettering,
Northamptonshire, NN16 8RE